Variation & Classification

- Read, engage and learn!
- Read the full colour, illustrated Topic Booklet.
- Use the Active Learning Game and Flashcards.
- Complete this Write Your Own Notes Booklet.

This Oaka™ Books Topic Booklet goes hand in hand with the Active Learning Pack on this topic. The pack includes a Write Your Own Notes Booklet, an Active Learning Game and Question & Answer Flashcards.

Fresh Focus on Learning

Variation & Classification Glossary

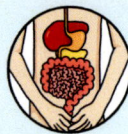 **Abdomen:** The lower part of an animal's body.

 **Classification Key:** System for sorting organisms into groups according to their characteristics.

Has gills? No Yes

 **Amphibian:** Cold blooded, vertebrate, reproduces in water, can live on land.

 **Discontinuous:** When a reading can **only** be one of a number of set choices e.g. male or female.

 **Animal:** Does **not** have cell walls. Has sensory and nervous systems that let it respond fast to stimuli.

 **Environment:** Surroundings in which a plant or animal lives.

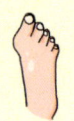 **Characteristics:** Features that animals or plants have.

 **Genes:** A set of instructions found in every cell. They tell the cell what it is and what it is like.

 **Classification:** Sorting living things into groups by characteristics.

 **Group:** Plants or animals that are like each other.

 **Cold Blooded:** Animals that can change temperature with their surroundings e.g. fish.

 **Identification:** Factors that tell you what something is.

 **Continuous:** When a reading can take any value along a scale e.g. height or weight.

 **Inherited:** Passed from generation to generation.

 **Correlation:** A link between two or more sets of data.

 **Insect:** Small invertebrate animal with 3 body segments and 6 legs. May have wings.

Variation & Classification Glossary

 **Interpret:** To understand the meaning of data.

 **Reptile:** An animal with scales that lives on land or in water.

 **Invertebrate:** Animals without a backbone.

 **Species:** Organisms that can breed. Their young can also breed e.g. all dogs are in the same species.

 **Kingdom:** The highest level of classification e.g. Animalia - all animals.

 **Specimen:** A sample from each species kept as an original to check others against.

 **Mammal:** Animal that has hair, or fur, and gives birth to live young.

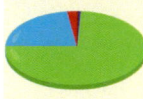 **Subdivide:** To split into smaller parts.

 **Offspring:** The young of organisms.

Mammals Fish Amphibians Reptiles Birds **Taxonomy:** The scientific system for identifying, naming and classifying organisms.

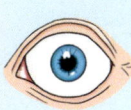 **Observe:** To watch carefully.

 **Variation:** Small, inherited differences in a species.

 **Organism:** Any living thing.

 **Vertebrate:** Animal with a backbone.

 **Plant:** They have rigid cell walls and produce their food by photosynthesis.

 **Warm Blooded:** Animal able to control it's own body temperature e.g. mammals and birds.

Variation in Species

1 — Species and Variation

- Living things of the same type belong to the same **species**.

- **Variation** means differences within a **species**.

- A dog is one **species**, but there are many different **types** of dog.

- Dalmation, Terrier and Labrador are all one **species**, but there is a lot of **variation** between them.

2 — Variation

- What **variation** is there in these domestic cats?

- Eye colour, size, colour and length of fur are all **variations**.

3 — Human Variation

- Humans are a **species**, but there is a lot of **variation** within our **species**.

- Eye and skin colour, height, arm span and blood group are all **variations**.

Variation in Species

4 What is a Species?

- **Species** often have very different **characteristics**. **But** some **species** are very similar, like horses and donkeys.

- It gets confusing, so we need a definition.

The definition we use is:

- A **species** is a group of **organisms** that can breed together and have **offspring**. The **offspring** can also breed.

- Horses and donkeys are **different** species. They can breed together, but their offspring (a mule) **cannot** breed. So, mules are not a species.

5 Characteristics

- Many **characteristics** are passed down from generation to generation.

- These **characteristics** are **inherited**.

- Skin colour, eye colour and hair colour are all **inherited** from our **biological** parents.

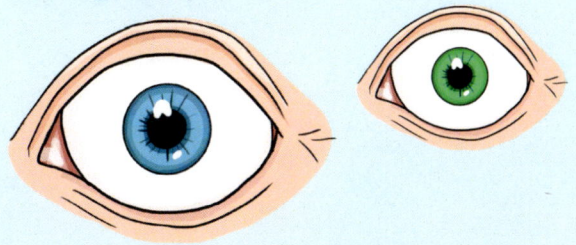

6 Inheriting Variation

But...

- We are not identical to either parent. We show **variations**.

Characteristics

7 Passing on Characteristics

- We **inherit** half of our **genetic makeup** from our father and half from our mother.

- These **inherited variations** are called **discontinuous variations**.

8 Control of Characteristics

- Your eye colour and some diseases are caused by **inherited** genetic information.

9 Male or Female?

- Your gender is **inherited variation**.

10 Inherited and Environmental

- **Variation** can be caused by **both inherited** and **environmental factors**.

- Twins who grow up in different places may show a lot of **variation**.

Environmental Factors

11 Environmental Factors

- Weather, diet and culture are all **environmental factors**.

- Environmental factors cause **continuous variation** in a species.

12 Environment and Variation

- Your hair may get lighter in the sun, and your skin may get darker (sun tan).

- Your **skin colour (tan), weight, religion and the language** you speak, are all **environmental variations**.

13 Environmental Factors and Plants

- **Environmental factors** cause variation in **plant**s too.

- One **species** of plant will have blue or pink flowers depending on the soil it is in.

Alkali
(P.H. above 7)

Acid
(P.H. below 7)

14 A Bit of Both

- Take two cuttings from the **same** plant.

- Grow one in **good** soil and the other in **poor** soil.

- The plants will grow **differently**.

Good Soil   Bad Soil

Discontinuous Variation

15   Discontinuous Variation

- **Discontinuous variation** is where characteristics can **only** fall into certain groups.

- You can **only** be male or female.

- Your blood group can **only** be AB, A, B or O.

16   Tally Chart

- We can use a tally chart to collect information (data) for **discontinuous variation**.

- We can then plot a graph from the data.

Blood Group	Number of People
A	卌 卌 卌
B	卌 卌 |
AB	卌 卌 卌 ||||
O	卌 卌 卌 ||

17   Discontinuous Variation

- We must use a bar chart to present our data.

- A bar chart is used to plot specific answers.

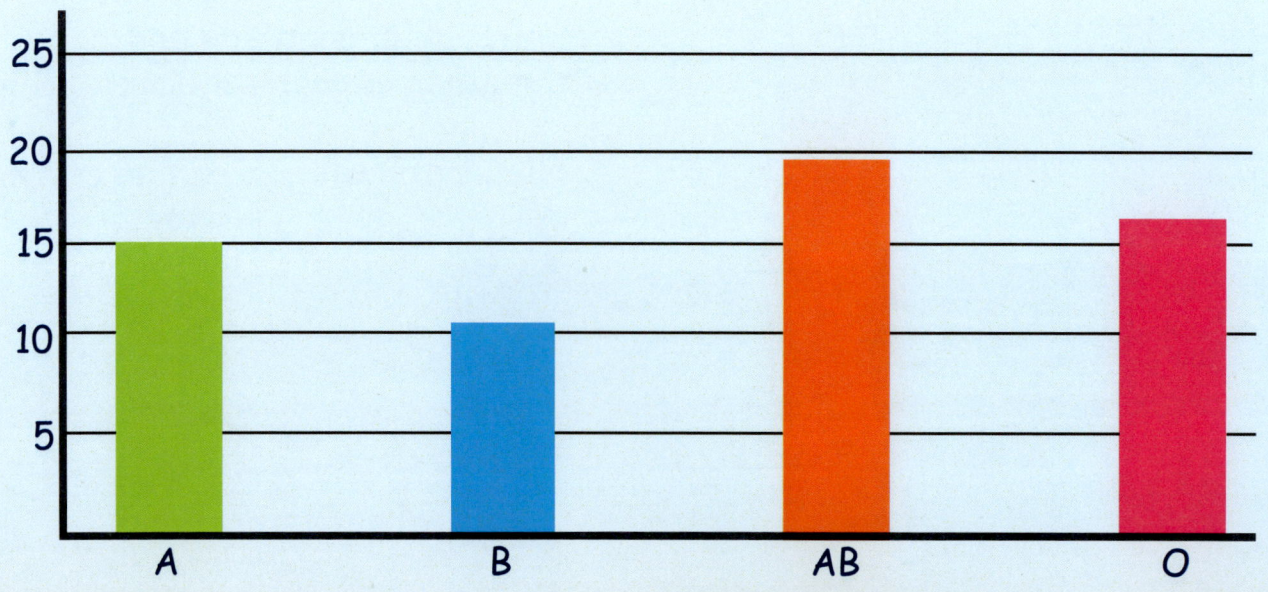

Continuous Variation

18 Continuous Variation

- When characteristics can fall **anywhere along a scale** they show **continuous variation**.

- For example foot size, height or weight.

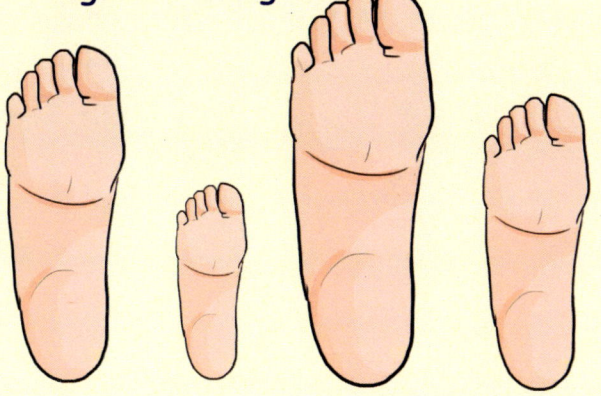

19 Continuous Variation and Environmental Factors

- Environmental factors affect continuous variation **more** than discontinuous (inherited) variations.

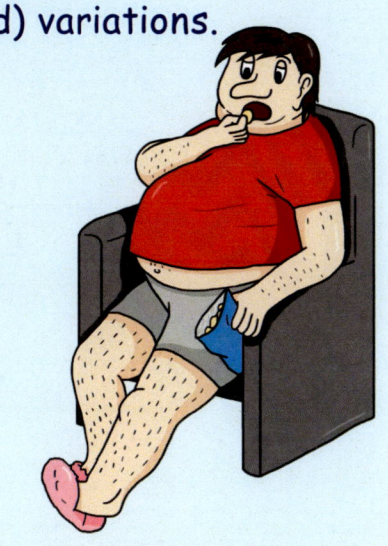

20 Collecting Continuous Data

- For **continuous data** like height, weight and foot length, we can still use a **tally chart**.

- As data changes **gradually**, we need **ranges** not just categories.

- The ranges we choose must be able to record **all** the data.

Height	Number of People
Up to 130cm	IIII
131-135cm	IIII IIII
136-140cm	IIII IIII IIII
141-145cm	IIII IIII IIII II
146-150cm	IIII IIII IIII
151-155cm	IIII IIII
156-160cm	IIII

Continuous Variation

21 Plotting Continuous Data

- We can then plot a graph from the data that we have collected.

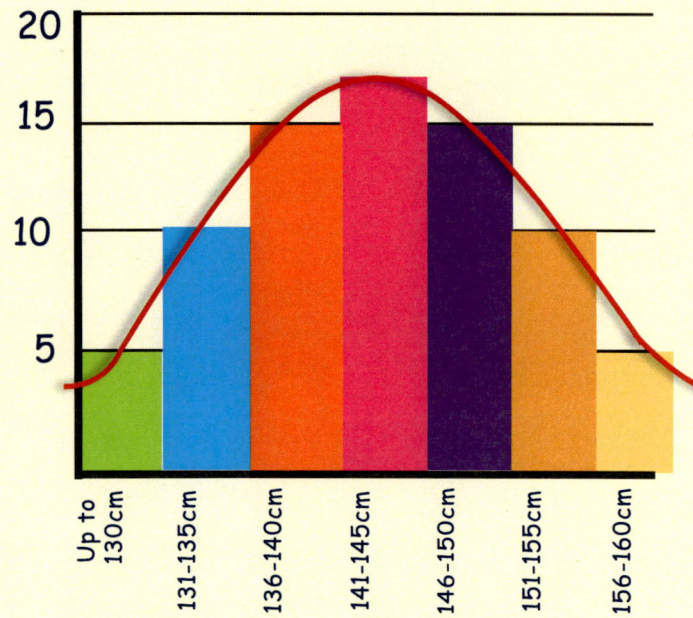

- A **histogram** is used to plot **groups of data**, for example how height changes in your form.

- If we draw a line that goes through the tops of all our columns, it makes a **bell shape**.

22 'Bell' Shape = Continuous Variation

- **Continuous variation** graphs **always** give us a **bell shape**.

- Sometimes the bell shape may be taller, or shorter, sometimes it may be pushed to one side, but it will always be there!

23 Correlations

- If there is a **link** between two or more sets of data, we say that there is a **correlation**.

- There is a **correlation** between the **distance** you walk and the **time** it takes you.

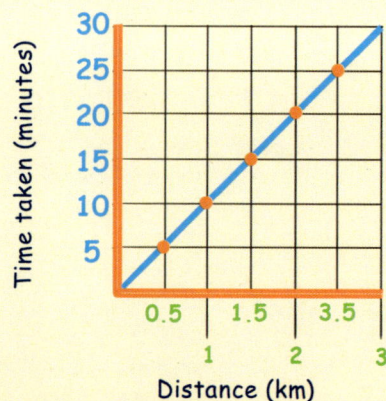

Correlations

24 — Why Are Correlations Important?

Correlations help answer questions.

- For example: if farmers feed their cows more, how much more milk will they produce?

25 — Making Changes

- **Selective breeding** is when only certain **examples** of a species are used for **breeding**.

- **Genetic Modification (GM)** is the **variation of genes** to make a certain **characteristic**.

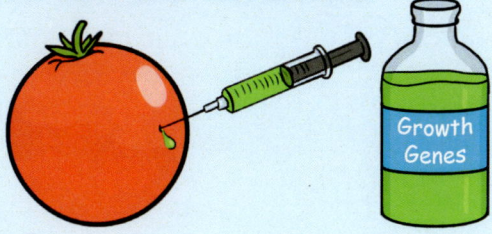

Growth Genes

- Think about the good **and** the bad effects of these.

26 — Looking At Features

- Lots of **species** look different but have a lot in common.

- A hippopotamus and a sheep look different but...

- They both have eyes and ears.

- They both have teeth for eating plants.

- They both give birth to live young.

- They both have a backbone.

Classification

27   Classification

- We can use common features to put **organisms** into **groups**.

- We call this **classification**.

- There are 5 major Kingdoms:

  - Animal
  - Plant
  - Fungi
  - Bacteria
  - Protists

28   The Animal Kingdom

- In the **Animal Kingdom** there are 5 groups of vertebrates:

1. Mammals

2. Birds

3. Reptiles

4. Amphibians

5. Fish

29   Animals

- **Mammals** include humans, monkeys, bats and dolphins.

- **Birds** include blackbirds, robins and eagles.

- **Reptiles** include lizards, crocodiles and snakes.

30   Animals

- **Amphibians** include frogs, toads and newts.

- **Fish** include goldfish, salmon and cod.

- Each group has common features.

Features of Vertebrates

31 Mammals

All **mammals**...

• have body hair or fur.

• give birth to live young.

• produce milk.

• are warm blooded.

• have a backbone
(they are **vertebrates**).

32 Birds

All **birds**...

• have feathers and wings.

• lay eggs with hard shells.

• breathe with lungs.

• are warm blooded.

• have a backbone (**vertebrates**).

33 Reptiles

All **reptiles**...

• have dry, scaly skin.

• lay eggs with shells.

• breathe with lungs.

• are cold blooded.

• have a backbone (**vertebrates**).

34 Amphibians

All **amphibians**...

• have moist skin.

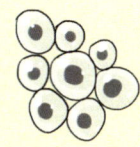

• lay their eggs in water.

• larvae have gills and live in water.

• adults have lungs and live
on land and in water.

• are cold blooded.

• have a backbone (**vertebrates**).

Features of Vertebrates

35   Fish

All **fish**...

- live in water.

- breathe with gills.

- have streamlined bodies.

- have bony skeletons.

- are cold blooded.

- have a back bone (**vertebrates**).

36   Vertebrates and Invertebrates

Animals are mainly broken into two groups:

- **Vertebrates**
  (Animals with a backbone)

- **Invertebrates**
  (Animals without a backbone)

Vertebrate (has a backbone)

Invertebrate (no backbone)

Invertebrates

37 Invertebrates

Most **invertebrates** have...

- a hard outer coating on the body (exoskeleton).
- eyes and a mouth.

38 Invertebrate Variations

- **Invertebrates** do **not** have a backbone.
- Spiders, insects, crustaceans, molluscs and worms are all **invertebrates**.
- Starfish (echinoderms) are also invertebrates!

39 Arachnids

- Spiders and ticks are arachnids.
- They have 8 legs.
- Body is in 2 parts.

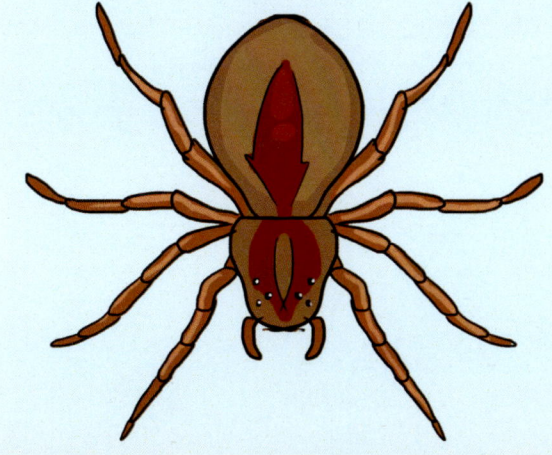

40 Insects

- They have 6 legs.
- 3 body parts (head, thorax, abdomen).
- 2 antennae.
- May have up to 2 pairs of wings.

This booklet is not to be photocopied. Thank you.

12

Features of Vertebrates

41 Crustaceans

- **Crustaceans** have different numbers of legs.

- Many live in the sea.

- Others, like woodlice, live on the land.

42 Worms

- Worms have long, tube-like bodies.

- They can be found living in many different places - underground, under the sea or inside other animals!

43 Molluscs

- Have a head, body and foot all as one part.

- This group includes snails, slugs and many sea organisms like mussels and oysters.

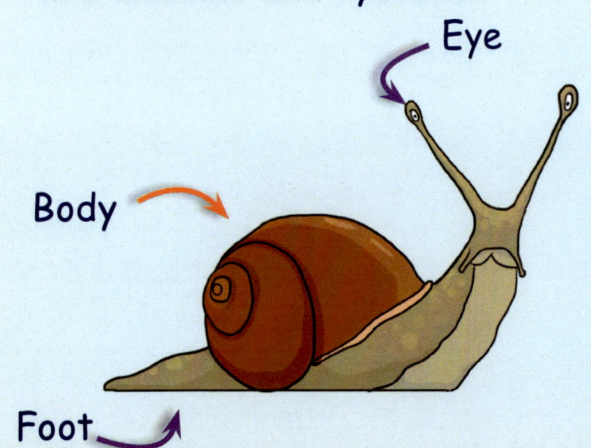

Eye

Body

Foot

44 Sorting Species

- There are millions of **species** on our planet.

- Many **organisms** have similar features.

- We use these features to classify them into their **kingdoms**, **classes** and **groups**.

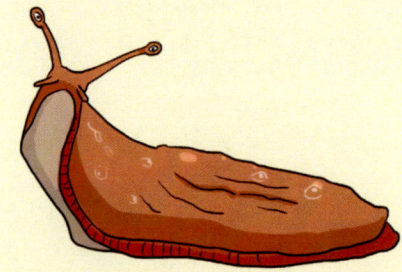

Recap!

45   Recap on Kingdoms

We can sort **organisms** into 5 major kingdoms.

1. **Animals**
2. **Plants**
3. **Fungi**
4. **Bacteria**
5. **Protists (anything that is not a plant, animal or fungus).**

46   Classification

Each **kingdom** is **subdivided** into smaller **groups**.

We have looked at 7 **groups** so far...
1. **Mammals**
2. **Reptiles**
3. **Amphibians**
4. **Birds**
5. **Fish**
6. **Vertebrates**
7. **Invertebrates**

Now, let's see where they all fit in.

47   The Five Kingdoms

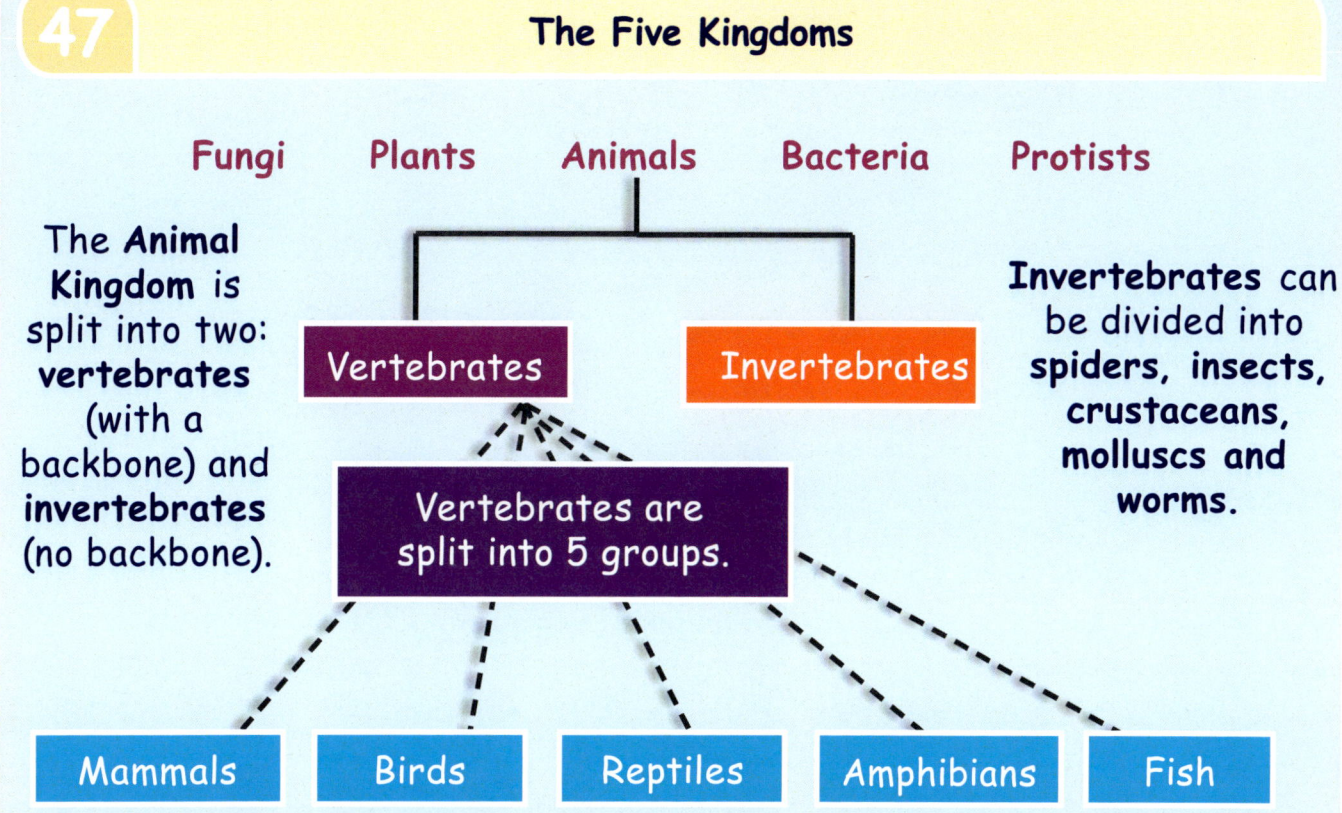

Fungi   Plants   Animals   Bacteria   Protists

The **Animal Kingdom** is split into two: **vertebrates** (with a backbone) and **invertebrates** (no backbone).

Vertebrates

Invertebrates

Invertebrates can be divided into **spiders, insects, crustaceans, molluscs and worms.**

Vertebrates are split into 5 groups.

Mammals   Birds   Reptiles   Amphibians   Fish

Classification Keys

Taxonomic Classification

- **Taxonomic Classification** is the **scientific system** for identifying, naming and classifying **organisms**.

- The same names for **organisms** are used all over the world.

Keys

- We use **keys** to identify, and put, **organisms** into their correct **groups**.

- A **key** is a set of questions needing a "yes" or "no" answer.

For example...

- Does the **animal** have dry, scaly skin?

- Does the **animal** live in water?

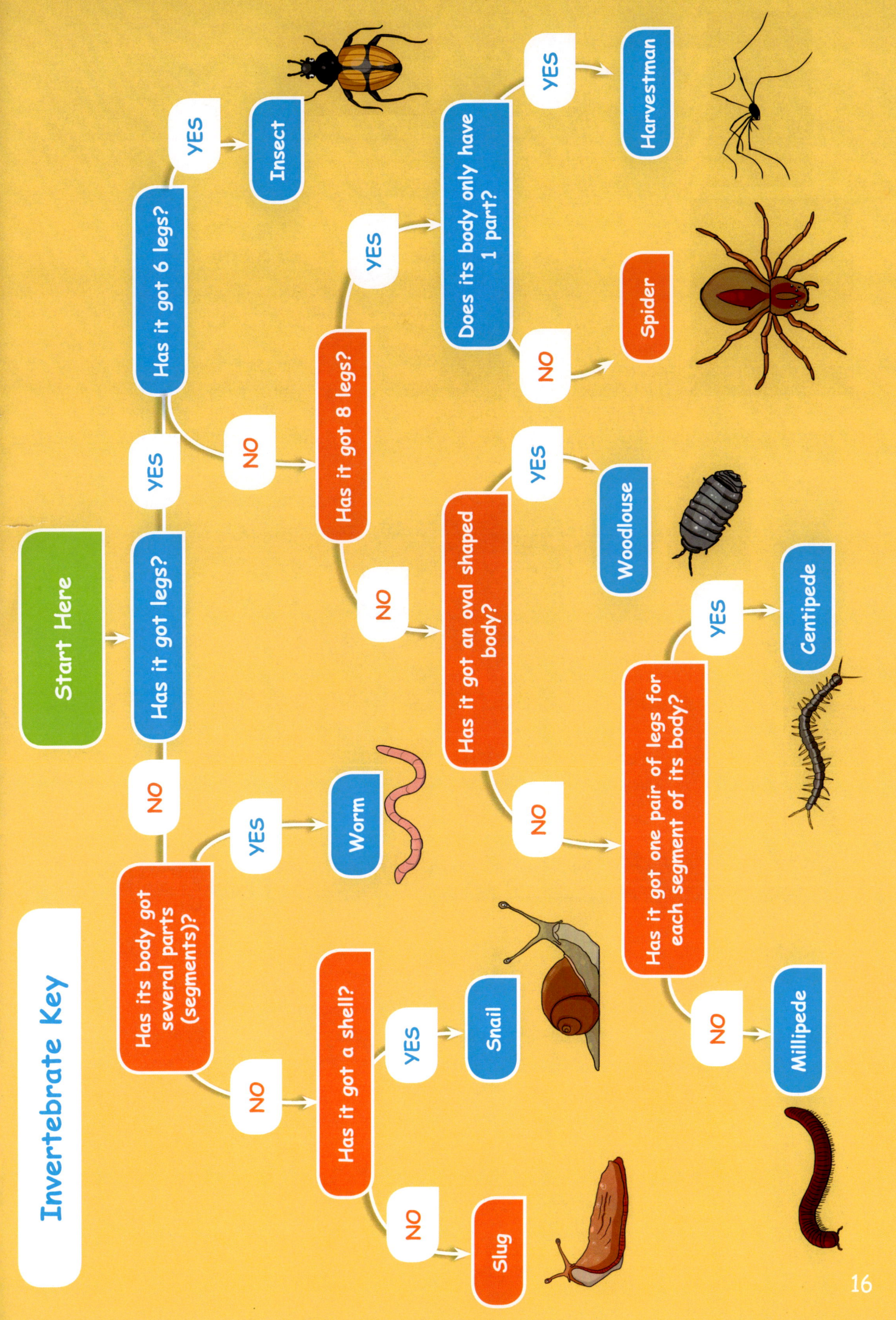

Invertebrate Key

Start Here → Has it got legs?

YES → Has it got 6 legs?
- **YES** → Insect
- **NO** → Has it got 8 legs?
  - **YES** → Does its body only have 1 part?
    - **YES** → Harvestman
    - **NO** → Spider
  - **NO** → Has it got an oval shaped body?
    - **YES** → Woodlouse
    - **NO** → Has it got one pair of legs for each segment of its body?
      - **YES** → Centipede
      - **NO** → Millipede

NO → Has its body got several parts (segments)?
- **YES** → Worm
- **NO** → Has it got a shell?
  - **YES** → Snail
  - **NO** → Slug

About Oaka Books

Children learn best when they are engaged...

Our aim is to help children enjoy learning by making it fun! That way they will succeed.

Following Common Entrance and National Curriculum guidelines for KS3.

Design and layout of our books follow guidelines from the British Dyslexia Association

Three Easy Steps

Read: the easy to follow bullet point Topic Booklet.

Engage: Play the Active Learning Game.

Learn: When you understand the topic, test yourself using the Write Your Own Notes Book. You can use the Topic Booklet to help if you get stuck.

One (short) Topic at a time:

For some students, a big book is a big turn off. That's why we focus on one topic at a time. Short and to the point.

Reading Age

This booklet is suitable for children with a reading age of 10 ½ years.

Topic Packs for KS1, KS2 & KS3 Include:

History
Geography
Chemistry
Biology
Physics

Please visit www.oakabooks.co.uk for more information about forthcoming titles

First paperback edition printed 2015 in the United Kingdom.
A catalogue record for this book is available from the British Library.

ISBN 978-1-909892-53-8

CE/KS3
Variation & Classifica-

Topic Booklet

ISBN 978-1-909892-53-8

Designed, set and published by Oaka™ Books.

To order other titles from Oaka™ Books, please email info@oakabooks.co.uk or visit www.oakabooks.co.uk, or phone: +44 (0) 2392 388519.

Acknowledgements
Our huge thanks go to the many teachers who have been involved in the development of this series of learning guides. Special thanks to Joy Gardiner, for producing hundreds of illustrations, to Kate Doehren, for her enthusiasm and invaluable assistance to my wonderful daughter Sophie, for being the inspiration for the books and, of course, to Charlie, for believing in them.

ISBN 978-1-909892-53-8
Produced in association with Kate Doehren, MA Ed, B.Ed Hons, RSA Dip, Sp LD/Dyslexia
Head of Learning Support, Hurstpierpoint College
© Copyright Oaka™ Books 2018